Life Beyond Loss

A Workbook For Incarcerated Men

Revised Edition

By Beverly Welo

FOUNDED 1870

American Correctional Association Staff

Richard L. Stalder, President
James A. Gondles, Jr., Executive Director
Gabriella M. Daley, Director, Communications and Publications
Leslie A. Maxam, Assistant Director, Communications and Publications
Alice Fins, Publications Managing Editor
Michael Kelly, Associate Editor
Sherry Wulfekuhle, Editorial Assistant
Dana M. Murray, Graphics and Production Manager
Traci F. Drake, Graphics and Production Associate

Cover design by Traci F. Drake

Printed in the United States of America by Graphic Communications, Inc.

ISBN 1-56991-016-2

This publication may be ordered from:
American Correctional Association
4380 Forbes Boulevard
Lanham, Maryland 20706-4322
1-800-222-5646

For information on publications and videos available from ACA, contact our worldwide web home page at: http://www.corrections.com/aca.

Cover photo provided by © 1994 PhotoDisc, Inc.

Table of Contents

Acknowledgments

I would like to thank the men I have worked with at the Lino Lakes Correctional Facility for everything they have shared with me and taught me. The quoted material in the margins is from these men.

I would also like to thank my supervisor, Peter J. Rieke, for encouraging me to pursue this project.

Thanks are also due to Heidi J. Gagnon, my friend, coworker, and cheerleader.

Thanks to Mr. Bill Murray, art teacher at Stillwater Correctional Facility, for the loan of the inmate art throughout this book. Thanks also to the inmates for their art.

Finally, I would like to thank my mother, Dorothy Elizabeth Welo. In her life (and since her death), my mother has taught me insight, compassion, tolerance, and love. Thanks, Mom.

Foreword

Life Beyond Loss offers corrections professionals a proven effective program for incarcerated men. This workbook provides imprisoned men with a rare opportunity to deal with their psychological issues—the ones that ultimately may keep them coming back to prison. In tested programs, this approach has lowered recidivism and reduced the incidence of disturbances in correctional facilities.

Its format is simple. Reading and comprehension required to do the exercises are at a fourth-grade level so that inmates at all stages of literacy may work through the ideas discussed. Though the language is simple, the ideas presented are complex. Many men have found in the exercises answers that have finally made sense to them.

We are proud to present this book because its format makes it easy to use while producing positive results. We are interested in your comments on this book and other of our ACA publications. Please direct your observations and remarks to ACA's Publications Managing Editor.

James A. Gondles, Jr.
Executive Director
American Correctional Association

Introduction

Everyone experiences pain and loss. Unresolved issues of loss can cause people to make negative choices, such as using violence or alcohol and other drugs to numb their pain. These same unresolved issues also may have prevented people, like you, from making it on the outside.

Both men and women experience the pain associated with loss. The expression of their pain, however, is generally different for men than women. Men often are denied the opportunity to express their pain openly. One way men are encouraged to hide their pain is by covering it with anger or rage. This raging griever is a danger to himself and others.

Men also are taught to be strong and in control. They may believe that expressing sadness will make them appear weak and out of control. Women do not face this pressure. To help men express the range of their feelings, which seem okay for women to show, this workbook is directed to men. You, too, have the right to explore your pain without the fear of being shamed for your efforts.

Feelings of rage, confusion, resentment, and the fear of experiencing the pain of grief, result in acting-out behaviors. Acting out (sexually, violently, or otherwise) seems to lessen the pain temporarily. *Life Beyond Loss* will give you another choice: working through your pain to healing.

Introduction to the Revised Edition

The basic text of *Life Beyond Loss* came about almost by accident. I had been teaching a grief and loss class in the prison at Lino Lakes, Minnesota for about a year. Unexpectedly, I was asked to help develop a new program in another part of the prison.

A colleague offered to cofacilitate the eight-week grief class; learn the ropes and keep the material available to the men in the old program. After a session or two, she asked me if I could write down some of the information. I slowly translated the eight weeks of class into the eight chapters of the workbook.

An inmate clerk typed it up and several months later photocopies were made available to some of the men at Lino Lakes. Case managers and chaplains gave copies to men who were struggling with the loss of loved ones. Inmates began to tell each other about the workbook and request copies.

A dear friend (the cheerleader mentioned in the acknowledgments) suggested I publish the workbook. I doubted that a publisher would be interested in grief work with incarcerated men. Nevertheless, I allowed myself to be persuaded to send the manuscript to the American Correctional Association.

There, the manuscript found its way into the capable hands of Alice Fins, who gently but firmly put the workbook into its present shape. More importantly, she listened to my ideas and shared the belief that loss and incarceration are linked to each other. She agreed that prisoners deserve the opportunity to work through their pain to healing.

The revisions and additional text have all come about as I continued my work at Lino Lakes. Thousands of men have used this material. They have taught me about the raging grief that has built layer by layer from childhood on to the present. They have shown me that they are able to challenge the beliefs that kept them from fully grieving over their losses. They have explained to me how acceptance of violence increased their tolerance to violence. Finally, they have shown me that their acknowledgment of their own pain is a pathway to developing compassion for others.

Grief and loss work is not a panacea for the problem of recidivism. It is one element of successful reoffense prevention.

Beverly Kay Welo
August 1998

Getting the Most
Out of This Workbook

You will get the most out of this workbook if you give yourself as much time as you need in each section. If possible, discuss issues that come up with someone you trust—someone who knows what you are going through and who can offer you real understanding. If a counselor or clergy person who you trust is available, talk to that person.

Use the extra space on each page to write notes to yourself or to jot down thoughts that are important to you. As you progress through the workbook, you can refer back to your notes.

If you identify an issue that means a lot to you, take time to explore it. Do not ignore it—it will not go away. Instead, it possibly will get worse. You may wish to seek professional help if you need it.

But, most of all, be honest with yourself.

Chapter One

Issues of Grief and Loss

The loss through death of a parent, a child, a friend, a lover, or any important person in our life brings about the feelings we associate with grief.

We experience many other losses in life besides death and dying. These losses, large and small, cause feelings of grief, as well.

This workbook looks at several issues almost all adults face. It also looks at one issue—the loss of personal freedom—that is specific to you, an incarcerated person.

I never knew there were so many griefs in my life.

This workbook covers ten major areas of grief and loss. In addition, you are encouraged to look at your own personal losses. The ten areas of grief and loss discussed include:

- loss of material goods
- loss of a job
- loss of the physical self
- loss of control
- loss of personal freedom
- loss of relationships
- loss of childhood
- loss of spirituality
- loss through death
- loss of dreams and goals

Loss of Material Goods

Losing material goods simply may be the loss of a favorite comfortable chair or the car on which you spent all your spare time and money. Or, it might be something that you pawned or that was stolen from you. Most people have experienced true grief over the loss of something material. Often, these things have little value to others, but a great value to us.

It is not simply the loss of the object that fuels your grief. You may have believed that your self-esteem would strengthen if you owned some special thing, or that other people would respect you for what you owned. "Things" never build genuine self-esteem, but the loss of some possessions can make your shaky self-esteem even less solid.

In our society, many people judge others by the "things" they have. You may have justified theft or a swindle by convincing yourself that you could not live without certain material goods. But, strangely enough, grief more often is triggered by small things. These include sentimental objects, such as photographs or souvenirs.

All incarcerated men have lost important objects in their lives. For example, during incarceration an inmate's personal possessions are handled many times, so more losses are bound to happen.

I never got over being a super jock in high school.

Addiction also has caused many incarcerated men to sell, pawn, or lose material things that were important to them. Try to imagine, for example, how many cars all of the men in your institution have lost. Think of all the suits of clothing, watches and jewelry, photographs, radios and TVs, and other things they have lost. You are surrounded by men who have lost most of their possessions, and the pain of those losses adds to the tension you feel around you.

Loss of a Job

You may complain about work, but if you have been laid off or fired (or even walked away from a job that was important to you), this is a grief issue for you.

Maybe you have noticed something in prison that surprises you—it feels good to work. It feels good to have a routine and get things done. It feels good to get praised, to learn new skills, and to have pride in your work. It feels good to be tired at the end of the day and (of course) it feels good to get paid!

Lots of incarcerated men never have worked before coming to prison. And they feel a sense of regret (a loss of past opportunities) when they look at the choices they made in the past.

Consider why the death rate for otherwise healthy men rises in the first twelve months after retirement. How are these deaths and grief related? Perhaps these men find their identity in their work. They lose much more than a paycheck when they end their work. They lose their role in life. If you had a job (and a role) that you were proud of, you undoubtedly know how painful this loss is.

Some men come to prison after leading a "double life." On the surface, they may have looked successful, but they were acting out (harming other people) in secret. If you led such a life on the street, this loss issue is especially important for you. You must prepare yourself for the reality of your return to society and the likelihood that you will not reach the same level of material success again.

Other types of jobs do not come with a paycheck. They include jobs such as being the best athlete in your high school. They carry prestige as their reward. If you had this role in high school, graduation may have been the start of a grieving process.

Sometimes it was the job (or role) of gang member, drug dealer, or hustler that brought about your incarceration. Even the loss of a job like this is a grief issue. But, if you do not learn new ways to make a living, you will come back to prison. Leaving the criminal life is not easy, but it is the only chance you have for real freedom.

Loss of the Physical Self

Some of your physical losses, like losing your hair, might seem funny to others. But this loss may be very serious to you. This grief issue deals with getting older—something every person goes through. It is also about illness. Some people are affected by these losses more than others. This issue is also about the actual loss of a body part: losing teeth in a fight, losing fingers in a work accident, or even being shot. All of these physical losses cause people to experience the cycle of grief.

After my dad died, I stayed drunk every day for a year. Then, I got busted, and I stayed full of rage.

Eventually, all of us will die. We are mortal. Each day you live with this knowledge and cope with it in your own way. Having a near-death experience brings your mortality strongly to mind. Discovering you have a physical illness or grieving over the death of a loved one also causes you to question your mortality.

Learning to accept your fears about death can help you see life differently. How would your life be different if you led each day as if it were your last day alive? Think of how precious each breath, each heartbeat would be. Is there someone of whom you would ask forgiveness? Is there someone you would forgive?

Some men have used this workbook to deal with their own dying. This is a grief no one can avoid. AIDS and other deadly illnesses are present in higher numbers among incarcerated men than in the general population. Again, addiction has contributed to this, as has homelessness. Also, as sentences are lengthening, many more men must deal with dying in prison. As you work your way through these exercises, you will find ways to meet your death and feel that you have "cleaned the slate" of your past.

Loss of Control

Loss of control is a different type of loss than the previous two. Loss of control is a loss of a part of yourself. Being able to control what you do and how you act is important. Being in control helps you feel safe. Being out of control usually means that someone or something else is controlling you. This is what happens during addiction to alcohol or to other drugs.

You may be addicted to a substance, such as cocaine or alcohol, or you may be addicted to a process, such as compulsive masturbation or gambling. If you experience loss of control, you experience addiction. If you experience addiction, you experience grief when you give up this addiction and go through a grieving process.

7

Addictions also involve love/hate relationships. Although you may feel relief at the end of an active addiction, you also may feel the loss of the substance or process that used to comfort you.

Many addicts want so much to forget the painful experiences they had while using chemicals that they pretend (to themselves and others) that giving up the substance was not a loss. If they are successful in blocking out the pain of their using, they are left with a longing for the "good times" and open to relapse. Addicts need the chance to grieve over the loss of their relationship with the chemical.

Even without using drugs, you can experience loss of control. Usually this happens with "emotional overload"—most often it is related to anger. If you have a history of violence and repeatedly have lost control, this issue is a particularly important one for you. Have you reacted to your loss of control by trying harder to keep yourself "in check?" You may tie yourself in knots as you hold in all of your angry feelings. Over time, these feelings build up until you again lose control.

If the source of your anger relates to your losses (in childhood, in relationships, or during incarceration), doing the exercises may help you untie the knots. You may discover that "softer" feelings, such as sadness, hurt, loneliness, or confusion, are hidden under your anger. This workbook is a safe place to look at those feelings and to reclaim them as a part of you.

Loss of Personal Freedom

Chapter five talks about the loss of personal freedom. The way you deal with the pain of being locked up has everything to do with your chances of staying out of prison after your release.

I tried to fill the hole in my heart with booze. It doesn't work.

This issue also is related to loss of control, since incarceration means living under the control of others. The loss of personal freedom also affects your family members who grieve (or hide their feelings) just as you do. As you work on this grief issue, you will become more aware of how your incarceration has affected others. This, in turn, will help make staying free an even more important priority for you.

If you have been locked up more than once, this is a very important issue for you. As hard as it may be for you to face up to it, you must admit that you chose to give up your personal freedom.

You might want to believe that you got an unlucky break—stop fooling yourself with this idea. If you have been locked up more than once, take a look around, you probably see some familiar faces. It is likely you have heard some familiar stories as well; "The cops are just after me," or "I had a lousy lawyer," or "I knew I couldn't beat it so I just took the time."

If staying free was your most important goal, you would have found a way to stay out of prison. Looking at everything you have lost by being locked up can help you to stay out of prison for good this time.

Loss of Relationships

If you are not still in a relationship with the first person you cared for, you have experienced this grief issue—loss of a relationship. For some, this loss comes through divorce. Others may grieve over the breakup of an intimate relationship outside of marriage.

Other important relationships that people grieve over include the loss of family ties. You may have experienced a "cut-off" from brothers and sisters, or from one or both parents. Sometimes these losses happened at a very young age. You may have been raised in foster families or group homes. You may have tried to bury your feelings about these early losses by telling yourself that the loss did not matter. Maybe it is hard for you to remember the "little guy" you once were, but he is the one who had to deal with these early losses.

Cut-offs affect us in a variety of ways. You may use the hurt you experienced as a reason to stay angry. You may think that because you have been cut off you do not dare to be close to people, or you may spend your time looking for substitutes to fill the empty space you feel inside of you.

Some typical substitutes include:
- using and abusing alcohol and other drugs
- being part of a compulsive relationship
- acting "macho" to frighten people away
- pretending not to care about someone important to you
- forcing someone to behave in a certain way in an intimate relationship. For example, this may include limiting another person's friends or church attendance and insisting that this person do things only with you and in your way. This will not bring the other person closer to you. Instead, this person is more likely to get angry with you and decide that he or she can live better without you.

Some men have gone so far as to hold people hostage. Some men even have been willing to take lives—saying "If I can't have you, nobody can." Others have learned to hold people hostage through drugs, prostitution, or shame. No matter what this looks like to the outside world, all of these actions are based on the fear of loss. A man who has to control his partner is operating out of fear—not strength.

If you have kept others in relationships with you against their will, learning about grief and loss can help you to see yourself differently. It also can help you to avoid repeating this behavior in your next relationship.

You have many important relationships in your life. You will experience some pain or separation with each one. In this workbook, you will look at ways to heal yourself from these old hurts and learn how to keep your new relationships strong and healthy.

The most important step in this process is admitting the pain of your original loss. You may be surprised to discover how old some of your hurts are. You may learn that your current pain is a reflection of an old loss.

Loss of Childhood

The loss of childhood is another grief issue. It means different things to each adult. For some, this loss is about not being taken care of anymore. For others, it is about holding resentments toward the people who should have taken care of you, but did not. Lots of children grow up too fast and have to take care of the grown-ups who should have been taking care of them. Some children are neglected or sexually or physically abused. All of these situations cause children to lose part of their childhoods.

As a child, you did the best you could with your pain and anger. Children lean toward healthy life—as plants lean toward the sun. But, all too often, the child's quest for a healthy life is blocked. Honoring your childhood losses is not about finding villains to blame for your current pain. It is about acknowledging the sources of your feelings and working through them to health.

If you believe you lost your childhood (or parts of your childhood), you have a true grief issue. If you have used your pain over the loss of your childhood to excuse violence or other acting-out behaviors, working through these losses can help you break your cycle of incarceration.

You may have acted out some of your childhood losses on children, stepchildren, or the children of your community. As you work through your grief, you may see this more clearly. You may have physically or sexually abused children to try to get over your own hurt. But the only way to get through pain is to face it squarely. For this reason, this workbook takes a serious look at the value of facing our pain, and the benefits that come with that difficult choice.

To be an adult—no matter how old you are—you need to close the door on childhood and accept adult responsibilities. This is a painful and difficult process. Many never close that door because they have not allowed themselves to grieve over their lost childhood.

Loss of Spirituality

Faith is often easier for children than adults. Some children have imaginary friends. Many believe in the tooth fairy or the bogeyman. If you have tried to bring your childhood ideas of spirituality into your adult life, you may believe that you have lost all of your faith.

If your idea of God (Higher Power, Great Spirit, Allah, or the Prophets) was a kind of tooth fairy/bogeyman, it may be time for you to come to a more adult understanding of spiritual things. Maybe you tried to order God around by making a bargain, "If you get me out of this, I'll be good." When you had to suffer the consequences, you might have blamed God. For some, loss of spirituality stems from a mistaken understanding of fairness. You want life to be fair, and when it is not, you may turn away from God.

Some people reject their Higher Power when they lose a loved one through death. This is very often the case when a child dies, or when the death seems especially "unfair." Sometimes the tendency to blame the Higher Power comes from the belief that your Higher Power has "taken" the person.

Some grievers later feel shame at having been angry at, or even hating, their Higher Power. The shame and fear may be so great that they believe their Higher Power will never forgive them.

If you have had this experience in the past, you can repair your relationship with your Higher Power. It will take time and the support of a spiritual mentor, but it can be accomplished.

As adults, you can regain your spiritual life. You can decide what parts of the picture do not fit anymore. You can leave the church of your childhood and find a new place to worship, or you can return with new insights and find your childhood church has changed, as well.

Not growing up with a lot of feeling words, it's hard for me to talk about them (feelings). I never felt I had a reason to talk about them. No one else cared about me. Why should I?

Loss through Death

You may be reading this book because you have lost a loved one through death. The loss may have been sudden and unexpected, or it may have come after a long illness. Even if the loss was not recent, you may continue to have many conflicting feelings about your loss.

Some common feelings for grievers include:
- sadness
- confusion
- loneliness
- anger
- guilt
- rage
- blame
- helplessness
- numbness
- relief
- fear
- shame

Ghosts   *Artist Unknown*

Most people can understand a griever's feelings if they look inside of themselves. But sometimes friends and family members act shocked or disgusted with the griever.

For example, it is common for grievers to be very angry (even rageful) at the person who died. It is also common for the griever to shame himself for feeling this way. If the people around him find his feelings uncomfortable, his shame is likely to increase.

None of your feelings is wrong. Sometimes, you might tell yourself you should not feel a certain way. You can twist yourself into knots trying to avoid feelings you do not like, but feelings are not right or wrong, good or bad. Feelings just are.

If you experience painful feelings because of the death of a loved one, it shows that you are a human being, capable of caring about another person. Sometimes you may have wished you were a robot, without any feelings. You may have used alcohol or other drugs to try to get away from feelings. The problem is you "come down" sooner or later. And, the feelings return.

It may well be that the greatest pain in life is the loss of a loved one. The pain takes many forms and can seem impossible to endure. To "resolve" such a loss never means forgetting your loved one. It does not mean being "over" the pain.

The resolution that the workbook can help you to reach is an end to acting out (violently, sexually, or otherwise) to avoid feeling your grief.

You may have additional complications of your grieving. Perhaps you were refused permission to attend a funeral. By concentrating your energy on being angry about missing the ceremony, you may feel "stuck" in your grief.

Other complications may include:
- hearing about your loss months or even years after it occurred
- having conflicting feelings about the deceased (a love/hate relationship)
- grieving for an aborted, miscarried, or stillborn child

I never knew grief was so many emotions. I have a long way to go in dealing with my grief issues.

You can resolve even these complicated griefs. It will take willingness on your part, but it can be done. This workbook can help you deal with your pain—if you let it. It will not make things the way they were before, but it can help you move back into life again.

Loss of Dreams and Goals

When you were a child, you had dreams and goals about what your life would be. Maybe you told people your dreams and they laughed at you. Maybe you set your own goals. Perhaps your parents, coaches, or juvenile workers set them for you.

Maybe you dreamed that you would be a sports star, and everyone would know your name. Maybe you dreamed that you would be a hero who rescued someone and won a medal. Maybe you dreamed that you would be a gangster, so you would never have to be afraid again. Maybe you dreamed that your parents would be proud, and you would be rich and successful.

Whatever you dreamed, it was not a dream that included the room you are sitting in today.

Do you remember your dreams? When all of your dreams have died, you truly "bottom out." You need faith to believe that your life can change. You need dreams and goals to make that change happen. If you are like the rest of the people on this planet, you have had disappointments as well as dreams and goals that fell through. All of the first nine grief and loss issues you just read about relate to the loss of dreams and goals. Resolving the grief issues one by one will help to give you back your dreams and goals.

Other Losses

Beyond the ten areas already mentioned are many other unique losses. Only you know exactly what they are. Give yourself the opportunity to look at all your losses, whether they were included in this list or not.

Examples of other grief issues include:
- being an immigrant and losing the comfort of your cultural ties
- being the child of a mentally ill parent
- going through combat experiences
- losing a much-loved pet
- failing to live up to your own (or others') expectations
- coping with a chronic illness

The list goes on and on. Try to be as clear with yourself about your losses as you can.

Exercises

You have read about ten types of losses:

- loss of material goods
- loss of a job
- loss of the physical self
- loss of control
- loss of personal freedom
- loss of relationships
- loss of childhood
- loss of spirituality
- loss through death
- loss of dreams and goals

Each of these losses is associated with grief. Grief is the collection of feelings, thoughts, and actions you experience regarding loss.

Ask yourself the following questions. Answer them in the space provided. As you answer these questions, remember that you have a right to each of your feelings, thoughts, and beliefs.

1. **Which of the ten grief issues would be hardest for you to share with other people? For example, I would be embarrassed to tell other people how I grieved over the loss of my car.**

_____

_____

_____

_____

_____

_____

_____

_____

2. **Which of the ten grief issues scares you the most? Why?**
   For example, I am very scared to look at my grief around my childhood. I always have covered it up and said it did not matter.

_____

_____

_____

_____

_____

_____

_____

_____

3. **What do you think about feelings of grief and sharing those feelings with others? For example, I think these are private. I do not want anyone else to know about them. I think I might "break down" or start to cry if I talked about them.**

_____

_____

_____

_____

_____

_____

_____

_____

_____

_____

As you answer these questions, remember that you have a right to each of your feelings, thoughts, and beliefs.

Chapter Two

The Modern View of Death and Loss

Your own experiences are your most powerful teachers. The funerals, wakes, or death vigils in which you have participated may seem like "normal" grief rituals. But, our culture affects each of these experiences.

Each of us is a member of one inescapable culture—twentieth century modern American. This culture defines your daily interaction with others.

Culture is reflected in:
  • mass-produced clothing: Levi jeans, Nike sneakers, T-shirts that advertise your favorite team
  • mass-produced reading materials: *USA Today* and *Sports Illustrated*
  • mass-produced music: Toni Braxton, Bush, Garth Brooks, and Puff Daddy
  • mass-produced movies: action films, love stories, and comedies
  • mass-produced food: Taco Bell, KFC, McDonald's

I drove 750 miles to my brother's funeral, but I didn't cry. I let my mother and sister cry.

Our sense of ourselves as Americans is defined by these and other aspects of our popular culture.

Everyone belongs to other groups or cultures, as well. These include membership with others of your ethnic heritage, your spiritual belief system, and your gender. Other groups to which you belong include associations with others who share your political beliefs and those who enjoy the same recreational activities.

Each of these cultures provides us with rules and roles. Many rules are unspoken, such as the rules of male and female behavior at a funeral or wake. In many cultures, it is acceptable for the woman to shed tears but not acceptable for the man to do this. Some cultures only allow the man to comfort the woman rather than display his own grief. Other rules are clearly stated (such as religious rules about eating or drinking). If we break these spoken or unspoken rules, we may believe that we have not lived up to our role in life.

We may feel shame if we believe that we have let our group down. It is always difficult to challenge the group's rules and roles.

The cultures of which you are a member can provide you with a feeling of belonging and safety, or they can leave you feeling "stuck" and unable to make free choices. You may choose to challenge your culture's beliefs. If your old beliefs are having a negative impact on your "quality of life" (and your ability to grieve), you need a new set of beliefs in order to make these changes.

Other types of cultures are subcultures under the wing of the larger twentieth century American culture. You may choose to identify yourself with a particular group by making a lifestyle decision, or you may find yourself in a particular group as a result of situations beyond your control.

Incarcerated people also form subcultures. Was your incarceration a part of your lifestyle choice, or was it a situation beyond your control? Your response to this question tells you whether you see yourself as a victim or an active participant in your own life.

Some subcultures include: bikers, hippies, punk rockers, addicts, inmates, recovering addicts, new agers, children, senior citizens, Hari Krishnas, white supremacists, black separatists, homeless people, people with AIDS, vegetarians, hunters, farmers, Republicans, bisexuals, college students, firefighters, or weight lifters. There are hundreds of subcultures in America. They are identified by what they wear, listen to, read, and eat (among other things). You identify yourself as a member of a group by your beliefs and actions.

The cultures and subcultures to which you belong have taught you a "normal" view of death. But, be aware that this view can change. In America today, the most common response to a death in the family is to turn all responsibility for the deceased person over to a mortuary. The only jobs left to the grievers are choosing the clothing the deceased will wear in the casket, choosing the casket, and writing an obituary. This was not always the case.

One hundred years ago there were many more jobs for the grievers. These jobs helped the family deal with the loss of their loved one. A man could use his skill and love in building a coffin or carving a marker. He could use his strength, anger, and sadness when clearing a plot and digging the grave for his family member. This was positive because many men are most comfortable with active grieving. They like to do something with their feelings.

I could see myself making a coffin, sweating over it, taking my anger and frustration out on every nail I pounded into it.

Conflicting feelings of sadness and anger are common during loss. Finding clear outlets for them are harder today than they used to be.

Formerly, the body was kept at home. The parlor of the farmhouse eventually gave way to the "funeral parlor" where professionals took over the grievers' jobs.

Can you imagine sleeping in the house where the body of a loved one lies in another room? Modern Americans are not used to this idea, but in our past it was seen as natural and healing.

Current culture separates us from death and dying. Many individual acts of grieving have been taken over by society because of the fear of death. Because people today often do not see the body—let alone touch it—it is easier to believe the death has not occurred. The ultimate example of this is the drive-in funeral parlor. You do not even have to get out of your car.

Think about the very public deaths of President John F. Kennedy and Elvis Presley. Rumors continued to persist for years that these two men were still alive. The unwillingness to believe that death has occurred is denial. Denial is a societywide problem.

Today, funerals often are very sterile events. The casket may be closed. The mourners often are encouraged to be very low key in their responses. This is especially true in some ethnic groups. In other types of death rituals, the relief and release available to grievers helps them to work through their grief.

Have you ever been able to let yourself scream and cry about the pain of a loss? Most men are too afraid of how others would react to let themselves show emotion this way. Have you ever punched a wall, smashed a car, or assaulted someone because of the pain of a loss? If so, can you afford to keep on dealing with your pain this way?

Styles of Grief

Men and women grieve differently. Men often are seen as the comforters of women. Who comforts the men?

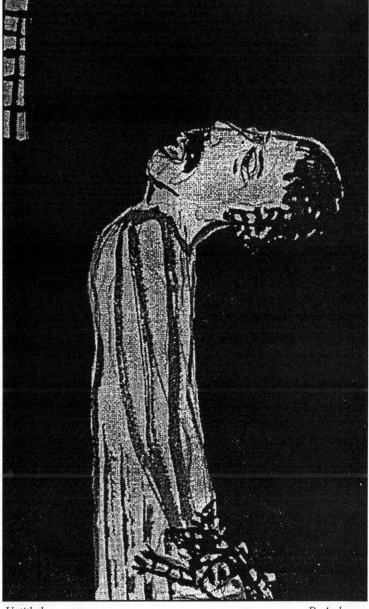

Untitled   *D. Anderson*

Men in our culture are taught to be strong—independent. This idea leaves a man little opportunity to ask for help. Today, more men are able to show their tears. Yet, a widower who does not cry is still described as "taking it well."

I have suffered a great deal, many personal and material losses.

What happens to the man who keeps his feelings inside? He becomes a pressure cooker. He holds in those emotions that he thinks are unacceptable.

If you leave prison a "pressure cooker," it will not take long before you blow yourself back inside. Admitting your feelings of grief (even in the privacy of the workbook) can be a release valve for you.

The one emotion that American men are allowed (even encouraged) to show is anger. Angry men are seen as strong men. The energy men gain from being angry helps them feel more in control. Many men fear that their sadness will make them feel out of control. Feeling out of control is scary. Many men will do almost anything to avoid this fear.

Are you really in control if you are a pressure cooker? No. Again, you might fool other people into thinking that you are tough, but inside you know that you could lose control at any time.

The modern view of death is one that tells males several things:
• Take care of others.
• Do not show your soft feelings (such as sadness, confusion, fear, or pain).
• Do something about the problem.

Since you cannot change the fact of death, you cannot do something about the problem. But showing anger and blaming others for the loss feels as though you are doing something. This showing anger and blaming is the protest phase of the grief cycle. Many men are stuck in this phase. They fear the sadness under the anger, so they stay stuck to avoid their pain. This is a catch-22. You cannot win. Men deserve more than this. Once you realize that death is not a problem you need to fix, you can allow yourself to grieve, and then move on.

Exercises

1. **Go back through this chapter, and reread all of the sentences that are written as questions. (The first one is "Was your incarceration a part of your lifestyle choices or a situation beyond your control?") Answer each question honestly.**

_____

_____

_____

_____

_____

_____

_____

_____

_____

_____

_____

_____

2. **Anger helps you to cover up emotions that you do not want others to see. What emotions do you cover with anger?**

_____

_____

_____

_____

_____

_____

_____

_____

_____

_____

_____

3. **What would happen if you let your guard down and shared your hidden feelings with someone else?**

_____

_____

_____

_____

_____

_____

4. **If you had the chance, would you want to grieve differently? Would it help you to make the coffin, build a funeral platform, or dig the grave? Imagine you are living 100 years ago. Write a story where you are allowed to be more involved in grieving over a family member or a friend.**

_____

_____

_____

_____

_____

_____

_____

_____

_____

_____

_____

_____

_____

_____

Chapter Three

Normal Life and the Cycle of Grief

What is a normal life? Who has had such a life? For many incarcerated men, normal life seems to be something that other people have had.

If you were raised during the 1950s or watch television reruns, you may believe that normal life was "Leave It To Beaver" or "Father Knows Best." Watching those programs, people saw a type of America that very few experienced at home.

In those television fantasies, and all the television fantasies since then, you saw people who had problems that could be solved in half an hour. You saw families where children were listened to, and painful losses (such as death and divorce) did not happen at all.

I thought something was wrong with me when I was a kid. My family wasn't "Happy Days."

Part of this television fantasy script, which many seem to believe in, is the idea that life is supposed to be fair. If we behave a certain way, good things will happen to us. Unfortunately, this is not true. You need to accept life on life's terms. In life, there is loss; with loss, there is grief.

Many incarcerated men have justified criminal behavior by claiming that life has been unfair to them. Owning the pain that life has given you can help to keep the people around you safe. It also can keep you free when you return to your community. As you learn about your losses, you will see your incarceration differently.

It appears that people can learn to deal with almost anything if they are taught how to react. When have you been taught how to grieve?

In the last chapter, you saw how death-experiences have been taken away from you. Once society turned death over to professionals, people lost the opportunity to teach their children how to grieve.

If you think about your school years, you probably can remember being taught some first aid. You know enough to put pressure on a bleeding wound, but very little about what to do when the pain is emotional. If your friend is bleeding, you can help him, but if your friend is crying, you feel helpless.

How did things get so confused? Grief and loss are common to everyone. So, why is grieving not as simple as breathing? Why don't we do it naturally?

Yet, you would grieve naturally, if you were not burdened by the ideas about what you should or should not do. As part of your growing up, you have learned some things about grief, but some of the things you have been taught are not true.

Here are some myths about grief and loss:
- Time heals all wounds.
- You can have it again.
- Big boys don't cry.

These myths are lies. They are convenient lies, because they keep grievers from making the people around them feel helpless. They serve the purpose of keeping the griever quiet.

Time Heals All Wounds

This is not true, and besides being untrue, it is a very hurtful thing to say to grievers. The truth is our wounds are our badges of adulthood. It is because we are wounded, that we can be compassionate toward others. Grievers who hear "time heals all wounds" think there is something wrong with them when they are not "good as new" shortly after a major loss. Time alone heals nothing. Healing comes from going through our pain and learning from it.

You Can Have It Again

This myth is about substitution. Little Johnny loses his puppy so daddy buys him a new one. The problem with this is that the new puppy is a substitute. Little Johnny never learns how to grieve over his original loss. When Little Johnny grows into Big John and his marriage is in trouble, he thinks he can substitute a new wife for the old one without ever admitting his loss. This may seem like a painless way to live, but there is a catch. If we are always ready to replace what we lose, we know that we are replaceable, too.

Each relationship is unique. The new baby does not take away the loss of the miscarried one. The new lover does not take away the old pain. And, the new friend does not make up for the loss of the old friend. Life will never be just like it was before, but we can reenter life—wounded, but stronger.

I've been shot. It ain't no fun. I'd rather be shot than let you see me cry.

Big Boys Don't Cry

This myth tells you that a man cannot be a real man if he cries. This lie is still being told to boys and men today. The truth is, crying is the greatest tool for healthy, normal grief. Denying this relief and release to men is terribly unfair.

Human tears have two very different functions. They clean the lens of the eye, and they provide release and relief from pain and fear. How can they do these different jobs? Research tells us that different tears do each job. The chemical content of tears made by onions is different from the tears created by

Untitled   *B. Church*

watching a late night rerun of *Old Yeller*. Human beings have this ability—unique among animals—to comfort themselves through tears.

This myth also makes men and boys feel ashamed of their tears. Shame is very close to anger. This explains why many men do not know when they are feeling the softer emotions of sadness, loneliness, and confusion. They have learned they will be shamed for these feelings so they hide them under anger.

As long as I never admitted she was gone, I didn't have to feel the pain.

How would you grieve if you did not know about these myths? Grief seems to follow a natural progression:
- denial of the loss
- protest of the loss
- grieving proper
- acceptance
- reinvestment

Go through these steps with an ordinary loss—the loss of a pen.

On the outside, losing a pen or pencil, a coffee cup, or a T-shirt might not make any difference. The loss would have to be bigger to be noticed. But, in prison, when so many possessions have been lost, even a very small loss can trigger strong responses.

Picture yourself reaching into the right-hand pocket of your jeans for the pen you left there. Your hand is in your pocket, but the pen is clearly not there. You reach into your left-hand pocket, your back pockets, your shirt pocket, and finally back to your right-hand pocket—even though you know it is not there! Maybe you turn the pocket inside out, or at least stick your hand back in there three or four times. This is denial.

You may stay in this stage of denial for a while. You might say things to yourself such as, "I know I haven't lost it," or "It's got to be here somewhere." You convince yourself that you have not lost anything. Eventually, you go through all the pockets in all your clothes. Then, you go through all your drawers. You look in places where you have never put a pen (such as under your pillow). Protest is next.

The protest phase feels like action to many men. It is a relief after the frustration of denial. Typically, if you have been alone with your frustration, this is the time you look for someone or something to blame.

Perhaps you remember you saw someone with a pen like yours in his hand earlier that day. If you don't like the guy, so much the better! You might directly confront him, or you might just be angry and not say anything. Sometimes, if you think you can get away with it, you might be tempted to take his pen as a substitute in the hopes of not having to deal with your loss.

Even though you now have admitted that the pen is gone, you do not think of it as lost. In the protest phase, you feel robbed. This gives you the chance to be angry, and anger gives you energy. You might get other people into the action at this point. One of the things you might say is, "That guy took my pen." This is easier than saying, "I lost it." Again, you want to be in control.

My wife and kids have been locked up as long as I have.

Perhaps you confront the guy, and he proves the pen isn't yours. Now, you feel stuck again. You may go back to denial and turn your room upside down. You may continue to protest and try to blame someone else. In fact, this is where a lot of men get stuck. The loss of a pen is added to all their other losses. It becomes the straw that broke the camel's back. This is why we hear stories that seem crazy about violence over "nothing."

You can get over being stuck by simply admitting "I lost it."

Grief Proper comes next.

Being in grief proper just means that you allow yourself to feel all of your feelings.

Here is a partial list of feelings you may have:
  • shame: "I lost something. How could I be so stupid!"
  • guilt: "If I had taken better care of it, I'd still have it."
  • fear: "Am I going crazy? I can't even hold on to stuff anymore."
  • sadness: "I wanted to write a letter to my kids, now I have to wait until I can get to the canteen again."

This is only a partial list, but it shows some of the feelings that are a part of grief proper.

Finally, you gain acceptance.

At this point, you accept your responsibility. "I lost the darn thing," and you put the situation in perspective. You may use your feelings to help you in the future. For example, you may tell yourself, "I'll take better care of my stuff," and then change the way you handle your things. This is the natural grief process. There are several "payoffs":

• You learn something.
• You gain acceptance.
• You make a healthy choice to do things differently.

Now, go back. Look at what would have happened if you had believed the myths about grieving.

Time Heals All Wounds. If you have been told this myth, you may respond to your loss by telling yourself, "I'll just forget about it." If you do not allow yourself to go through the cycle, you do not forget about it. What you probably do is get upset or angry. You might take your upset feelings out on someone else. This sideways anger can get you in lots of trouble. As you try to forget, you probably struggle with feeling ripped off. This adds to a generally negative outlook on life.

You Can Have It Again. If you buy the myth of substitution, you just go out and look for another pen or pencil. Maybe you rob someone or con them into giving you theirs. Substitution always seems as if it is working, but if you never admit your personal responsibility for your losses, you do not learn how to avoid making the same mistakes over and over again.

Big Boys Don't Cry. This response does not suggest that you burst into tears about losing a pen! What is suggested here is that part of this myth tells men not to feel anything when they lose in life. Look back over the suggested list of feelings that losing anything might bring out in a man. Think about your loss and see if you went through each of these feelings. It is your right to have all of these feelings and then resolve them by learning about yourself and your actions.

If a man can go through all of these changes because of the loss of such a small item, it is easy to see how explosive he can become over more serious losses. No matter the loss, the course of dealing with it is much the same. If you learned to deal with loss by being angry or full of rage, it will be difficult to learn a new course of action. Difficult, but not impossible.

Exercises

1. **When you were little, was it "okay" for you to be sad about a loss? Were you shamed for feeling sad or crying?**

_____

_____

_____

_____

_____

_____

2. **What is the first major loss you can remember? For example, the death of a pet, a friend moving away, or the divorce of your parents.**

_____

_____

_____

_____

_____

_____

3a. **Follow the cycle of grief with that first loss. Did you complete the cycle or get stuck? If you got stuck, where did you stop the cycle?**
   • denial
   • protest
   • grief proper
   • acceptance

_____

_____

_____

_____

_____

_____

3b. Did someone tell you a myth about grief?

_____

_____

_____

_____

_____

_____

3c. Did someone try to substitute something for your loss?

_____

_____

_____

_____

_____

Chapter Four

Pain Avoidance and Substance Abuse

You have looked briefly at the cycle of natural grieving. You saw how that cycle is interrupted by the myths you have learned about grief and loss. In this chapter, you will look more closely at the reason you so willingly allow your natural grief to be interrupted. This is your wish for pain avoidance.

In our culture, we value looking good. No matter how you are feeling on the inside, you try to look like nothing is bothering you. You want to be "cool." Cool is a way of life. Cool people, especially cool men, are mask-like—they show very little expression on their faces.

If being cool is important, you avoid emotions that will take away your mask. Some of those emotions include: sadness, happiness, and fear. When you experience a loss, you still look cool as long as you stay angry. This is another way of understanding how you can get stuck in the protest phase.

No one has ever seen me cry. No one will ever see me cry, but my pillow knows better.

If anger is not enough to keep you from feeling your pain, you may turn to medication: alcohol or other drugs.

Another reason you avoid pain is because you think that it has no value. There is value in human suffering, but you may not have been taught this in any clear way.

This chapter will help you look at how all of these things work together in the loss of relationships.

These grief-cycle interrupters include:
- avoiding pain
- being cool
- abusing substances

Each person has his "sore spots." One way to think about sore spots is to think of a puncture wound. If you step on a nail, for example, the wound on the surface probably will heal up right away. The problem with a puncture wound is that it may be infected far below the surface. Old hurts, unresolved grief issues, and resentments often are hidden this way, too. You might look fine on the outside, but you know that you are festering inside. You might feel this as a deep pain that shame will not let you share with other people.

This may be unresolved grief over the memory of relationships that "broke up." Many people have found themselves trapped in a cycle of unsatisfying relationships. You may stay in some of these relationships for years. Others

Double Think   *F. Armell*

may be very short. You will be looking at ways to break this cycle using the "natural" grieving process.

One way to avoid the pain associated with loss of relationships is to have only "surface" connections with other people. You can do this even in relationships that appear to be intimate by not sharing your feelings with your partners. For most people, this is a learned behavior.

Learned behaviors come from watching others deal with their situations and making the decision to deal with our situations the same way.

You have seen many examples of men dealing with relationships. Sometimes you have observed them firsthand—like watching your father deal with your mother. Sometimes you observed relationships at a distance—like watching Clint Eastwood in the movies. Either way, it is likely that you very rarely saw men who were able to share their feelings of grief freely.

I repressed and medicated my past griefs.

When their first relationship breaks up, boys are more likely to complete the natural grief cycle than adult men who have learned more myths about grief and feel uncomfortable displaying their emotions. However, if you shared your feelings with other boys, it is likely that your grief was interrupted. Instead of moving through the cycle, you probably got stuck. If you began sharing feelings of sadness, your friends may have said, "She was no good." You may have been told to substitute: "There's more fish in the sea." Or, you may have been encouraged to stay in the protest stage by hearing that you were robbed: "So-and-so took your girl."

The people who turned you away from your feelings often wanted to save you from your pain. They also may have wanted to stop your pain so that they would not be uncomfortable with their feelings. Again, you have the right to your feelings, even if they make other people uncomfortable.

When you grieve about the end of a relationship, one of the first things you may do is to start a new relationship (substitution).

After a divorce or break up many people are encouraged to start a substitute relationship immediately. This helps their friends feel better and takes the griever's mind off of his loss.

There are several problems with dealing with grief in this way:
1. The new person is not seen on his or her own merit. This new person just functions as a "pain killer."
2. You are likely to place much less value on the new relationship to protect yourself.
3. You may try to force your new partner into submitting to you. You do this believing that this person will not be able to "get away."

The overall result of these actions is that you lose your ability to trust your partner. This, in turn, robs the relationship of intimacy. Your partner will sense this lack of intimacy and feel that he or she is not valued but trapped by your needs.

Normal, healthy people will not want to stay in such a relationship. They will leave you. When the relationship ends (because of your inability to be intimate), you may continue to blame your partner. Many people go through life in this fashion. You may blame your partner for not meeting all of your unresolved grief needs.

My pain is the only thing I own free and clear. Now, I know it's worth something.

If this cycle is familiar, you may feel helpless and think there is no way out. Fortunately, there is a way out of this vicious cycle—moving through the original pain.

Step-by-step, working through the "normal" grief cycle, you can free yourself from the pattern. To do this, you must first learn more about the value of human suffering.

The value of human suffering has several dimensions:
1. Working through your pain will allow you to experience compassion for the pain of others.
2. You will receive increased self-esteem when you work through a painful situation, instead of avoiding it.

Many men realize that their self-esteem is not strong. In prison, they may enter a chemical dependency program, hoping the counselors can restore their missing sense of self-esteem.

No one else can do this for you. The path to self-esteem comes from doing the right thing. This is the only thing that makes people feel good about themselves. If you are leading a double life, conning people inside and outside of prison, you probably feel shaky. Doing the right thing (even when it is painful) is the only way to get stronger.

Facing pain honestly is doing the right thing.

3. You will accept the world in a more realistic way when you stop running from pain.

Take a hard, honest look at what you have lost in life. This will make everything (and everybody) that you have left in your life become more precious to you. People respect the realistic man who does not live in a world of delusion.

4. Finally, you will become stronger and healthier because you have survived the experience.

Many incarcerated men spend a lot of time becoming physically stronger in prison. They show a lot of self-discipline as they try to attain their goals. That strength can attract people to you who like the surface look of who you are. Emotional strength attracts people who see beneath the surface.

If you make the decision to go back through your original pain, you need to believe that your pain will be worthwhile.

Now look at each dimension more closely:
1. Working through pain allows you to experience compassion for the pain of others.

Compassion for others is one of the most attractive traits a potential partner has. You may have adopted a self-centered and cynical view of the world out of fear. To break the cycle of unhealthy relationships, showing compassion for the pain of others is the first step. To do this you need to use the knowledge that you have gained about your own pain and understand how others may be hurt or stuck.

I didn't get the chance to say good-bye. I didn't know I could say it anytime, anywhere.

2. You receive increased self-esteem.

Self-esteem is another trait that is very attractive to healthy people. You show your healthy self-esteem by taking care of yourself and dropping your phony, cynical fronts. With healthy self-esteem, you no longer need to pretend you are made of stone. You can share feelings (including self-doubt) with potential partners.

3. You accept the world in a more realistic way.

By accepting the world in a more realistic way, you no longer try to make potential partners be "perfect." No individual can fulfill all your needs. It is unrealistic for you to search for a partner who will do this. It is unfair for you to demand this from someone else. Again, it is very attractive to potential partners to see you as a realistic person who is able to feel fulfilled in a variety of ways—not just through this one exclusive relationship.

4. You become stronger and healthier.

The healthier you are, the healthier the people you attract are. Healthy people are more able to build committed relationships. They are more worthy of your trust.

All of these dimensions of the value of human suffering have one thing in common—they make you more attractive to potential healthy partners. These are the very people you most want in your life.

To stop the cycle of unsatisfying relationships requires some creative grief work. First, identify the relationship(s) over which you have not allowed yourself to fully grieve. Do not be surprised if you discover that the relationship you find yourself stuck in ended many years ago. Consider writing a good-bye letter to that person. This is not a letter that you would send in the mail, but a grief exercise to help you see how the relationship has kept you stuck. Figure A on the next page is an example of such a letter. It was written by an inmate to his daughter who died of Sudden Infant Death Syndrome (SIDS) at the age of two months.

After you finish your letter, put it aside. Further instructions on this assignment occur at the end of chapters six and seven.

Chemicals—including alcohol and other drugs—are an important part of the pain avoidance in our culture. Using chemicals to avoid pain is another learned behavior. Television and the movies provide many examples of people drinking when they are in pain. "I need a drink" seems to be the solution to stressful situations in our culture.

Starting at a very young age, many people try to deal with pain through drinking alcohol or by using other drugs. Using chemicals also lowers our inhibitions (our sense of acceptable behavior). This often enables a person to say or do things he would never do if he were sober.

It is very important for you to assess your chemical health before you continue to actively work through your unresolved grief issues. If you are currently using legal or illegal drugs in any amount, you must stop. If you cannot stop using chemicals, you must get help to do so before you continue your grief work. This is absolutely necessary if you are to receive any relief from this process. The only exception to this is prescribed medications. If you are currently seeing a psychologist and taking your medications as prescribed, your grief work will not be negatively affected.

Figure A. Good-bye letter

November 15

To my darling daughter Ashley,

Hello my little pumpkin! Ashley, I have so many things I would like to say to you. First, I want to tell you I love you very much, and I miss you so bad it hurts.

When you were here with me, I was so very happy and excited. All I had to do was look at you and I would smile and I would be filled with a happiness I never had before. I can honestly say "I was truly happy."

You being born gave me a purpose in life. A responsibility I would never give up for anything. I would have done anything or given anything to make you healthy, happy, and loved.

Baby, I know in my heart, you were happy. You knew you were loved. I saw it in your beautiful smile when I would pick you up at Auntie Melissa's after work. Your smile seemed to say, "Yeah, Daddy's here."

You were everything to me pumpkin. I remember singing to you in the car. Remember the song I would always sing to you? "Ashley Rose, Ashley, Ashley Rose, the prettiest girl I know. From her head down to her toes. She's Ashley Rose, Ashely, Ashley Rose. I love that girl so, from her head down to her toes."

Remember when we would play the elevator game? You always laughed a lot.

Oh Baby, I miss those times we had together so very much. When you moved on, a part of me died also. I was so angry, and I was so hurt. I couldn't understand why you were taken from me. I lost control after you went away. I didn't care if I lived or died. Pumpkin, I don't like feeling that way, and I don't think you would want Daddy to be so sad and hurt. That's why I'm writing this letter to you. I want to get better.

Baby, nobody will ever take your place in my heart. You are still there and will be forever. I don't think I will ever find that special happiness only you could give me, but I know I can find other things or people that can make me happy.

You are special, pumpkin, nothing or nobody will ever replace you. You are still, and will always be, Daddy's little pumpkin. I miss you Ashley Rose.

Although we didn't have alot of time with each other, we loved each other very much and for that I am greateful!

I will always miss you baby, and I will never forget the special time we had together or the wonderfull joy you gave to me.

Even though you are gone, your love and your memory will live inside of me forever. Thank you pumpkin, because even though you are not here, you are still helping me to feel better and you still give me the courage to go on.

All my love to you,

Daddy

Exercises

1. Have you ever known a man who allowed himself to work all the way through the grief cycle (denial, protest, grief proper, and acceptance) before he entered a new relationship? Write about seeing this process. Include your feelings about seeing another man grieve. (If you have never seen this, write a story about a relationship ending and a man going through the complete grief cycle.)

_____

_____

_____

_____

_____

_____

_____

_____

_____

_____

_____

_____

2. Do you believe in the value of human suffering? Look back through this chapter. Are these ideas new to you? Pick one example of a grief from which you ran away. How would your life be different if you had known that your pain had value?

_____

_____

_____

_____

_____

_____

_____

_____

_____

_____

_____

3a. What is your current chemical health? Are you now using substances?

_____

_____

_____

_____

_____

_____

_____

_____

3b. Have you used chemicals (including alcohol or other drugs) to avoid the pain of ending relationships? Give an example:

_____

_____

_____

_____

_____

_____

_____

_____

3c. If you are in recovery (formerly an active addict/alcoholic), have you allowed yourself to grieve over the loss of your chemicals?

_____

_____

_____

_____

_____

_____

_____

_____

3d. Describe your grief issues with chemicals. Are you stuck?
- denial
- protest
- grief proper
- acceptance

_____

_____

_____

_____

_____

_____

_____

_____

_____

_____

_____

_____

_____

_____

_____

_____

_____

Chapter Five

Grief and Incarceration

As discussed in the first chapter of this workbook, the way you deal with the pain of being locked up has everything to do with your chances of staying out of further or new incarceration. This chapter concerns grief and incarceration. You will be able to gauge your progress through the grief cycle by reading this chapter and completing the exercises at the end of the chapter.

There are so many losses tied to being in prison that it is hard to add them all up. But, one way or another, most prison losses are tied to the loss of dreams and goals. For example, being unable to watch your son growing up is not only the loss of that relationship—it is also the loss of the dream of being a dad.

The loss of freedom, of movement, of speeding down the highway— this is the grief of incarceration.

Most people do not want to face up to the fact that they have made mistakes. In this way, incarcerated men are no different from anyone else. Because people do not want to admit they made bad choices, they may pretend the consequences are not painful.

This is why a man will say that prison is "nothing" or boast he could do another five years "standing on my head." This is why some incarcerated men refuse to admit their crimes: if they admit what they did was wrong, they fear that life in prison would be unbearable.

You are going to read how one man struggled with these issues. If his experiences sound like yours, pay attention to the ways you have behaved in the past.

John Jones was twenty-five years old. One Friday night he went to his neighborhood bar with a few of his buddies from work. Everybody was feeling good. After a few rounds of beer, John began harassing his friend, Bob, about being late for work that morning.

John felt that Bob missed the humor in the situation, so he added a few choice words about Bob's wife, as well. What John did not realize was that Bob and his wife were having lots of problems. Bob was very worried about the future of the relationship. He was late for work because he and his wife were arguing. John kept teasing until Bob punched him in the nose.

Soon, everyone in the bar chose sides. Before they knew what had happened, John and his pals were out in the snow while Bob and his buddies bellied up to the bar.

John's friends decided that they had enough fun for one night. John was alone in the parking lot with the bottle from his glove compartment and thoughts of revenge to keep him warm. A few hours later, when Bob left the

Merry Christmas   B.R. Raymond

bar, he ran into John's fist (which was still holding the bottle), and Bob fell over a snowbank unconscious.

John decided it was time to go, and he left the parking lot. Bob lay in the snow for several hours until he was spotted by a cruiser and taken to the hospital. Luckily, Bob lived, but John was booked on a first-degree assault charge.

Denial — "I have not lost."

To his wife, his lawyer, and all of his friends, John maintained his denial. But what is really amazing is that he maintained it to himself as well. Bob was his friend. Why would he leave him in the snowbank? He did not remember doing it. He was not the type of guy who would do a thing like that.

This way John did not have to admit his loss of control. He did not have to look at how he had become an alcoholic. He did not have to admit that he had ended his friendship with Bob in an alcoholic rage. There were lots of payoffs for John to stay in denial.

I didn't think I'd get caught. When I was busted, I thought I could beat the case. When I came into prison, it was like a bad dream.

Since he is in denial about his actions, he is also in denial about his incarceration. Both before and during his trial, he tells his wife that he will be home for their anniversary. He tells his boss to hold his job. He cannot understand why his boss refuses. When the verdict comes down, he is stunned and confused. As he is taken from the jail to the prison, his anger begins to mount.

Protest — "I was ripped off."

When denial starts to crumble, people experience fear. Fear is very uncomfortable (and shameful) for many men. It feels good to get mad. It feels powerful.

At this stage, during the ride to prison, John picks a fight with one of the guys and blames Bob for all of his problems. He now suspects he did it—but it was not his fault.

Occasionally, John slips back into the denial phase and tries to interest his lawyer in filing an appeal. He convinces his wife to ask his relatives for a loan. The lawyer (once the money is raised) agrees to file the appeal. John is back in the denial phase. When the appeal fails, John blames the lawyer and moves back into the protest phase.

John is very angry. He lets the staff know it by his attitudes and his actions. He starts to get write-ups. He does some segregation time. Now, he is more angry. More write-ups and more segregation time follow.

One day in segregation, with nothing to do, John lets himself think back over his life. He begins to feel some of his sadness. He gets very scared by this. He is afraid he will break down. He is afraid that he might start to cry. He is also afraid that he almost did kill his friend. He is afraid he really is in prison (something he never allowed himself to think of before). He is afraid that his wife will leave him if he stops denying his crime. He is afraid that he is going crazy. He is afraid if he lets himself be sad that he will have to kill himself. He is afraid to kill himself, but he also is afraid to live with himself.

Once out of segregation, John buys some dope. He decides to stay high until the day he leaves. Staying high, working, and being angry keeps away his "bad" feelings. Months go by, and John tests positive for drug use. His caseworker insists that he get into chemical dependency treatment. John's wife has not been too happy with him lately, so he tells her he is going to clean up his act. He checks into the chemical dependency unit.

John gets into trouble right away. The anger that seemed normal in the cell halls is way out of line in the treatment unit. John does not want to get kicked out of treatment in the first week, so he drops his "in-your-face" attitude. Within days, he is starting to feel just like he did in segregation.

John is at the crossroad. At bottom, John is not a "bad" person. He is a human being who has made mistakes. He needs to decide if he is going to continue his pain avoidance or face up to himself. John asks for a one-on-one with his counselor. For the first time since the night in the bar, he admits what he did.

It's okay to cry as opposed to getting high. In my new understanding, I don't medicate myself into that bottomless pit of addiction.

Grief Proper — "I lost, it hurt."

John is moving into grief proper as he levels with his counselor. The weeks and months that follow are the most painful time of John's life. His emotions bounce up and down like a roller-coaster. Sometimes in his bed, and once in his chemical dependency group, he cries. He hates to cry. He is ashamed of his tears, and he does not believe the other guys when they tell him it is okay to cry. Gradually, he admits to himself that he felt some relief from crying.

One day in group, another man starts to cry when talking about his crime. John surprises himself when he tells him, "It's okay, I've been there too." Once he says it, he knows it is true.

John has a lot of work to do with his family and friends. They stuck by him during his denial. When he starts to come clean with them, they are all very angry. Some get over it. Some do not. Bob surprises him the most. He forgives John.

His wife is tired of all the changes. She leaves him. John moves all the way back through the grief cycle over his divorce. He often wants to get high. He often thinks that the pain will never end. He often wishes he could go back, but he knows too much about himself now.

Acceptance — "I lost, it hurt, I survived."

It is a position of strength to say, "I survived." It is much more powerful than the anger of, "I was ripped off." It is much more realistic than, "I have not lost."

John keeps working on his feelings, as well as talking and writing about them. Gradually, he moves into acceptance.

He talks about his losses:
- I lost control.
- I lost relationships.
- I lost my personal freedom.
- I lost material goods.
- I lost my job.

If I loved being out on the street so much, how come I kept getting locked up?

He admits it hurt to lose these things. Then, he takes stock of himself. He talks about what he gained:
- I gained sobriety.
- I made the relationships I kept stronger.

He decides:
- When I get out, I will value my freedom more.
- I can work and get other material things, and I will value them more.
- I can get another job.

Finally, he admits, "I lost. I hurt. I survived." When he leaves prison, he is healthier and stronger than he ever has been.

However, John does not live "happily ever after." No one does. His life continues to have ups and downs. He has the same types of griefs all people do. The difference for John is that he knows he can handle some pain. He knows that he can survive.

Most incarcerated people are not as lucky as John. Most get stuck and stay stuck. Some stay in denial—filing appeals and appearing "virtuous" and victimized. Others, perhaps most, stay stuck in protest—always angry, always defiant, always looking for someone or something to blame. When these people leave prison, they feel robbed. They want someone to pay. The recidivism cycle continues.

When you are released, you will have your freedom. What value will you place on it?

Incarcerated people are not the only ones who are locked up. To work through your anger, think of others who also have lost their freedom.

Think for a moment about the elderly in high-rises and "old folks homes." Many have lost their mobility and are unable to leave, or they are afraid to leave because of unsafe streets. Think of the thousands of people confined to beds in hospitals. Think of the mentally ill. You are never unique in your suffering.

Exercises

1. Where are you in your cycle of grief over your incarceration? (You may be in several different stages.)
- denial — "I have not lost."
- protest — "I was ripped off."
- grief proper — "I lost, it hurt."
- acceptance — "I lost, it hurt, I survived."

_____

_____

_____

2. If you are stuck, what are you willing to do to move on?

_____

_____

_____

_____

_____

_____

3. What grief issues are you avoiding today? How would your life be different if you allowed yourself to grieve?

_____

_____

_____

_____

_____

_____

_____

_____

Chapter Six

Denial and Protest

This chapter explores the first two phases of the grief cycle: denial and protest.

All of the grief phases have both positive and negative aspects. You do not need to shame yourself if you find that you are stuck in one phase of the cycle. But you do need to understand what is keeping you from moving forward and resolving your grief issues. Usually we are kept stuck by two forces: comfort and fear. We are comfortable where we are stuck because it is familiar to us. We are afraid to move on because we doubt that we will be able to cope with our feelings.

Denial — "I have not lost."

The Positive Aspects of Denial

The denial phase is important and helpful to us because it protects us from emotional overload. If we suffered severe losses as children (for example, being institutionalized), our denial of the pain helped us cope with our unfamiliar surroundings. In fact, children always struggle to be healthy. It is when we keep our childish beliefs in adulthood that we become unhealthy.

What scares me the most is loss of relationships. I told myself I didn't have any real friends. I told myself it didn't matter when they left, they weren't real friends anyway.

Another way to look at the benefit of denial is to picture a car accident where both partners of a married couple are seriously injured. It may be his denial of the extent of his injuries that allows the husband to function long enough to rescue his wife from the burning car.

Denial of feelings gives us the same ability to move through difficult emotional situations.

The Negative Aspects of Denial

The negative aspects of denial surface when it continues after it has outlived its usefulness. Think of a child institutionalized at an early age. During his stay, his denial helped him to cope. But if he never acknowledges the pain, sadness, loneliness, fear, and confusion he felt, he cuts himself off from his own humanity. Often, he will adopt a view of the world that tells him nothing is of value. No one can be trusted. He does this believing he never again will be hurt. Unfortunately, there is a major problem with this view of the world. It is untrue.

Some things have value. Some people can be trusted. However, the griever is not able to sort out which is which. His denial shuts out the positive as well as the negative.

Trustworthy people may enter his life, but they will leave when he shows his distrust. Each broken relationship fulfills his belief.

If we treat the world (and the people in it) poorly, the world will respond by showing us just how awful it can be. This is called a "self-fulfilling prophecy." We become the agents of our continual disappointment.

Everybody I cared about died. Then, I died, I just kept walking around.

Returning to the couple in the car accident, denial of the extent of his physical injuries only sustains the man as long as his adrenaline keeps him upright. He usually will collapse once he and his partner are safe. If he continues to move about, he probably will injure himself more severely.

Emotionally, you do not always get the same cues that your body offers your physical self. You injure yourself more severely because of prolonged denial.

Your denial takes many forms. In the end of a relationship, for example, one of the partners simply may refuse to believe what has happened. One partner may file for divorce while the other continues to make plans for a shared vacation. In extreme examples, one partner may hold the other against his or her will, demanding that the relationship continue.

Denial is one of the clearest symptoms of chemical dependency. The addict may lose his home, the trust of his family, his job, his money, and even his physical health, and continue to deny that his drug use has caused his losses.

Denial also can be described as "sincere delusion." While all of the people around the griever see that a situation is hopeless, the griever may continue to convince himself otherwise.

The antidote for denial is the reality check. If you believe you may be in denial about a loss, you can check it out with someone who is not as emotionally involved in the situation.

For example, John tells everyone that his wife will stand by him during his incarceration, but he has some nagging doubts. He does a reality check with his friend, Bill.

John is likely to hear some unpleasant truths if his doubts are correct:
1. Bill might point out that a restraining order is not a welcome mat.

2. Bill may mention that no visits in three months is not a good sign.

3. Bill may ask if John has ever asked his wife if he will be welcomed home.

The last piece is especially important. People in denial often avoid asking the questions they need answered because they are afraid of the answers.

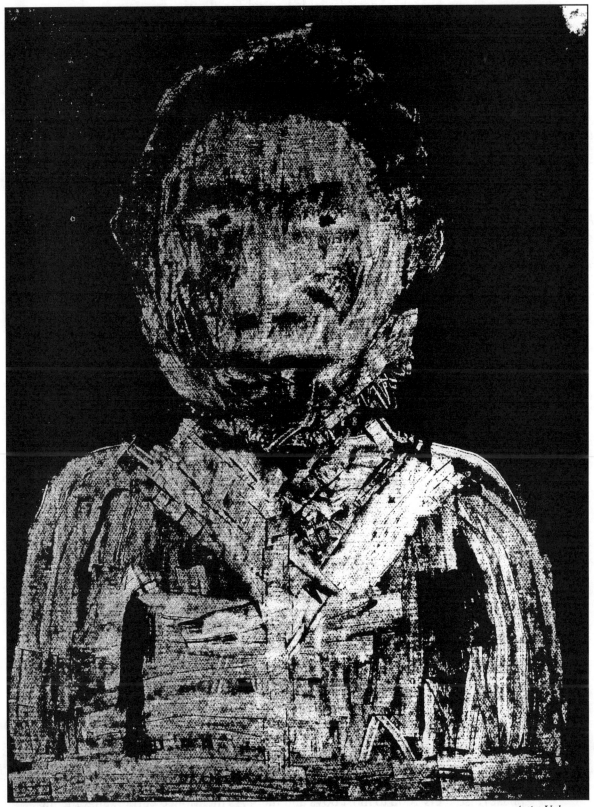

Untitled   *Artist Unknown*

As you have seen, denial has both positive and negative aspects. It is important to remember that some denial is natural for all grievers.

Long after you believe you have moved through your denial, you may find yourself drawn back to it. The grieving process is not a simple step-by-step advance. You will find yourself sliding back to the earlier stages from time to time.

Trying to rush yourself through the cycle is one reason you slide back. Sickness, additional losses, lack of sleep, and other stress may also cause this reversal.

If I admit it's over, I have to look at what I did. I'm not ready for that.

Once again, you do not need to shame yourself or gauge your progress by other people's timetables. If you have returned to the denial stage, you can decide when the time is right to move on.

Admitting to yourself that you are in denial is the first step to moving through it. Ask yourself what you gain from staying in denial: comfort, power, self-esteem? Whatever the answer is, only you can decide when you are ready to leave your denial behind.

Ask yourself what you might gain from no longer denying your loss. Would it be the chance to move ahead? A better (more realistic) set of goals? The knowledge that a problem was resolved? Only when the new gains outweigh the old will you be ready to move on.

Protest — "I was ripped off."

The Positive Aspects of Protest

Anger is a natural human emotion. It does provide us with energy. This energy is useful—at times.

In the example of the institutionalized child, anger may be very helpful in his situation. Perhaps he was institutionalized because his parents neglected him. Because even abused and neglected children instinctively love their parents, most children find it very difficult to be angry with them. His anger most often will be directed at the social worker who took him out of his home and at the staff of the institution in which he is being kept.

His anger gives him the energy to deal with his situation. If he had stayed stuck in his denial, he may have had little or no energy. Anger (in the protest phase) also feels good to most boys and men. As mentioned earlier, anger is the one emotion boys and men are expected to show in our society. The institutionalized boy will get support from his peers for expressing his anger.

Finally (and most importantly), his anger is justified. All grievers have the right to feel and express some anger over their losses.

Return to the couple in the car accident, and examine their positive protest phase. A crowd has gathered around the injured couple. One or both of them is very likely to demand that someone call 911. If no one seems to be responding, their anger and protest will give them the energy to keep demanding the help that they need.

Protesting your losses shows a great deal about how important the loss is to you. Although the emotion you reveal is most often anger, the deeper feelings of sadness and hurt are often apparent to people closest to you as you protest.

Some of you will take the energy you receive from your anger and throw yourself into work or other projects relating to your grief. Again, returning to the couple who had the accident, after the accident they protest to improve the bad road conditions in the intersection where their accident occurred. This valuable protest may result in new signs or signals being installed. This would be a healthy use of their energy. It even may save lives.

The Negative Aspects of Protest

During the protest phase, you look for a scapegoat (someone to blame for your pain). Sometimes you choose people or systems that have nothing to do with your situation.

At the end of a relationship, for example, you may blame your parents, friends, or your ex's new partner. You do this to avoid taking responsibility for your part in the breakup. You also may blame your ex-partner for all of the relationship problems. It is unrealistic to think that all of the problems in any relationship come from just one partner.

Looking for scapegoats results in other life choices, as well. If you have stayed locked in the protest phase, you may have become part of a movement or organization that protests (and blames) certain groups for society's problems. You may have targeted ethnic groups or religious groups. You may have singled out a gender (men or women) and blamed that gender for all of your pain. You may have singled out a class (wealthy, middle class, or the poor) and scapegoated it. All of these ways of looking at the world can allow you to feel superior to some parts of society. You may have accused an ethnic, religious, gender, or class group of having robbed you.

Feeling robbed or ripped off is common in the protest phase. The problem with continuing to feel this way is that it keeps you from owning the reality of having lost something or someone precious to you.

The anger which comes from the protest phase also can turn explosive and result in violence to yourself and other people. Violence turned inward can be seen in increased drug and alcohol use, self-mutilation, poor self-care, and even suicide attempts.

The danger of suicide for the griever is greatest at the end of the protest phase. The griever may be feeling helpless and hopeless, and suicide may seem the only way out. Drug overdoses that result in death may be direct suicide attempts or come about because the griever keeps increasing the amounts of drugs used in an effort to avoid his feelings.

If you are experiencing thoughts or plans about suicide, please tell someone. Your thoughts are a temporary part of the grief process—suicide is permanent. Your life is valuable regardless of your experiences.

I know I'm alcoholic, but I still protest. I had good times while using.

Violence and criminal behavior also may occur as the griever turns his rage on others. The violence may be directed at friends and family or strangers. Because of the explosive nature of rage, the griever may be shocked at his own actions. Continued violence leads to ever greater violence as the griever becomes "numb," and violence becomes normal.

The griever may begin to develop a "tolerance" for violence. Tolerance has to do with being willing to continue with something, or allow it to go on. For example, if he is violent with a person, he might begin with verbal abuse, then a slap, then a closed fist, and finally a weapon. Tolerance to violence increases like tolerance to a drug.

After a while, violence is normal. Can you afford to tolerate violence? Are you more or less likely to return to prison if you use violence to solve your problems?

The raging griever may turn his protest against his whole community. He may rob because he believes he was robbed, for example. This cycle of violence and criminal activity inevitably ends with the griever suffering even greater losses (such as the loss of personal freedom or the loss of his life), as society moves to protect itself from the griever's rage.

In the following exercises, you will examine your own denial and protest with regard to two grief issues. Before you begin the exercises, turn back to the first chapter of the workbook. Select two of the ten major grief areas. Give yourself some time to consider the issues with which you will work. If you have some issues you do not feel ready to challenge yourself on, put them aside for now. You may prefer to use the exercises to look at issues that presently are not as painful.

_____

Exercises

1. **If you wrote good-bye letters (as suggested in chapter four) to people you had ended relationships with earlier, reread the letters and ask yourself the following questions. If you did not write such a good-bye letter earlier, do so now.**
   Was I in denial when I wrote this?

   _____

   _____

   Am I still in denial at this time?

   _____

   _____

   What do I gain from staying in denial?

   _____

   _____

   What could I gain from moving on?

   _____

   _____

   Was I in the protest stage when I wrote this?

   _____

   _____

   Am I still protesting at this time?

   _____

   _____

   What do I gain from my protest?

   _____

   _____

   What could I gain from moving on?

   _____

   _____

2. Choose two grief issues and ask yourself the following questions about each:

Issue one:

How long did the denial phase last?

_____

_____

What purpose did denying your loss serve you?

_____

_____

_____

What kinds of feelings surfaced for you during the denial phase?

_____

_____

_____

How did you avoid acknowledging your loss?

_____

_____

_____

Did other people try to break through your denial? If so, how did they try to reach you?

_____

_____

_____

How long did the protest phase last?

_____

_____

_____

Do you occasionally find yourself still protesting this loss?

_____

_____

_____

Did your anger take the form of self-destructive behavior? If so, how did you try to harm yourself?

_____

_____

_____

Did you single out scapegoats for your anger? Who were these people/systems?

_____

_____

_____

Did you engage in violence or criminal acts during this protest phase? If so, what were they?

_____

_____

Issue two:
How long did the denial phase last?

_____

_____

_____

What purpose did denying your loss serve you?

_____

_____

_____

What kinds of feelings surfaced for you during the denial phase?

_____

_____

_____

How did you avoid acknowledging your loss?

_____

_____

_____

Did other people try to break through your denial? If so, how did they try to reach you?

_____

_____

_____

How long did the protest phase last?

_____

_____

_____

Do you occasionally find yourself still protesting this loss?

_____

_____

_____

Did your anger take the form of self-destructive behavior? If so, how did you try to harm yourself?

_____

_____

_____

Did you single out scapegoats for your anger? Who were these people/systems?

_____

_____

_____

Did you engage in violence or criminal acts during this protest phase? If so, what were they?

_____

_____

_____

Chapter Seven

Grief Proper and Acceptance

This chapter explores the third and fourth phases of the grief cycle: grief proper and acceptance. Even while you are denying or protesting a loss, you are doing grief work. The third phase, grief proper, is the time of your most active grieving. That is, your energy and actions are directed toward moving through your pain and resolving to adjust yourself to life after loss.

Grief Proper — "I lost, it hurt."

The Positive Aspects of Grief Proper

True grieving is both a powerful and beautiful experience. It is powerful because you are pulled through a painful and humbling process. It is beautiful because this process brings you in touch with your ability to love.

It was a relief to let it all out.

The depth of your grief will be in proportion to the importance of the loss you are grieving. You honor your losses by your feelings and actions in grief proper.

The griever enters grief proper by shedding his earlier anger while still being fearful of his ability to survive his pain. Another fear the griever may experience is that letting go of anger may feel like not caring about the loss. Staying mad at the doctors in the hospital where a loved one died may feel like a tribute, but hanging on to anger seriously can affect your judgment. For this reason, the move to grief proper often brings you clarity.

Return to the example of the institutionalized boy, mentioned in chapter six. Imagine his passage to grief proper. He has become dissatisfied with his angry and cynical view of the world. Perhaps some trustworthy person has revealed a different worldview to him.

His grief work may begin with that trusted person, or it may begin after a "crossroads" experience, such as a near-fatal drug overdose.

Often, his first experience with grief proper will be accompanied by tears. Since boys and men so often have been told that their tears are unacceptable, the boy may feel shame for his tears and move back to the protest phase to feel his anger energy again.

However, these tears also may bring the boy some feelings of relief and release. Grief proper truly has begun with these tears. Because of this, he may allow himself private tears again.

Untitled   *Artist Unknown*

For most people, deep grieving is a private issue. For children, especially, it is less demanding to do the deepest levels of grieving alone—because they do not need to explain their pain. Isolating oneself while grieving is very common. The griever may wish to explore his loss very deeply, and he may feel that others would be bored by constant reference to the loss.

As you explore your grief, what will you feel? Many grievers describe waves of sadness. As each wave passes over you, you will feel the pain of your sadness, but you also will learn that you have the strength to bear it.

In the example of the boy, he allows himself to feel sad about the loss of his home life. He probably also will encounter true anger over his loss. Unlike the sideways anger of his protest phase, this anger will be focused more appropriately. Because he has accepted his sadness, he will be able to be angry with the actions of his parents. This type of anger is self-esteem building because it reveals to him that he has value, and he has the right to be sad about the loss of his home. He will see his parents more clearly, and he may realize that he even can hate their actions while still loving them.

Knowing my son will be ten years old when I get out, I can't deal with it. I've lost those years with him. I just pretended I didn't care.

During this time, he will continue to explore other feelings as well, including fear. Deep grieving does involve fear. The griever is confronting life without something or someone he has considered necessary. But because he has admitted his sadness by saying, "It is sad that I was taken out of my home," and raised his self-esteem by saying, "I deserved more than the neglect that brought me here," he can deal with his fears by looking for others who are worthy of his trust.

This is very different from the substitution that was discussed in the third chapter. The boy is not seeking to replace his mother or father. He is not believing the myth, "You can have it again."

What the griever is doing in this process is learning that his painful loss has not denied him the chance to love and trust again. He may find other adults who can be trusted. He will value himself enough to know that he deserves love and trust in his life. The griever will continue until the natural conclusion of this whole process. At this time, his isolation will end, and he will reach out for help from others.

The Negative Aspects of Grief Proper

While grieving freely has many positive effects, there is the potential for the griever to become stuck in this part of the cycle, as well.

Part of the fear that grievers encounter in grief proper may contribute to the grievers being stuck. The griever fears this loss may be his fault. In divorce and other family-stress situations, many children fear that they have caused the problems. During the protest phase, this fear may surface in statements that begin with "If only . . . ."

"If only I had gotten better grades, my father wouldn't drink so much." "If only I were a better son, my parents would have treated me better," and so forth.

During grief proper, this type of thinking may return. This will drive the griever deeper into isolation. Too much isolation keeps the griever from moving into acceptance, because he is afraid to admit his secret fears.

Another fear that grievers face is the fear of their own death. If you truly allow yourself to grieve the loss of a loved one, you are also dealing with the fact that your own life is short. Each of us will die. The book you hold will "live" long after the author has died. Illness or injury can claim lives in a moment. Mourning the loss of a loved one will not prevent your own death, but it will help you to see how you will live on in the thoughts of others.

I'm proud of myself because I made it through this.

You must never put a timetable on your passage through the grief cycle, because you may shame yourself for your "slowness." But if you have exhausted yourself with your sadness, you may have to admit your fears to someone else in order to move forward. If you believe that you are harming yourself by being overwhelmed with grief, reach out to someone for help. A chaplain, a psychologist, a counselor, or a doctor may be available to you. If you know of any trustworthy friend, he or she may be able to help you ease out of your emotional isolation.

It is hard to end isolation. It takes courage to reach out to others, but if you have come this far in the workbook, it is clear that you have courage. Good luck in finding someone in whom to confide.

Acceptance — "I lost, it hurt, I survived."

The Positive Aspects of Acceptance

The key word for the griever in the acceptance phase is reality. Acceptance of loss allows the griever to say, "I lost. I hurt. I survived."

The griever can say, "I lost" without the nagging doubt of, "I was robbed." He can acknowledge, "I hurt" because he values the pain he has gone through in grief proper. When he says, "I survived," he is aware that his true strength does not have to come from the energy of anger.

What does it mean to accept a loss?
- You are truly honest when you admit to yourself (accept) that something or someone of value has gone from your life.
- You own your loss by acknowledging that your life has changed forever.
- You experience yourself as a valuable human being because your ability to grieve has shown you that you have the ability to love.
- You are more compassionate than ever before as you recognize your fellow grievers, each with his or her own pain.

In your acceptance, you experience all of these: honesty, ownership of your loss, value of yourself, and compassion for others. These are all goals worth working toward.

During the acceptance phase of the grief cycle, the griever will be likely to employ greater creativity in the grieving process. For example, accepting the loss of a loved one might allow a griever to assemble photographs or mementos and display them. These objects may have been too painful for the griever to see earlier in the grief cycle.

Acceptance of your loss does not imply forgetting the loss or never feeling sadness regarding the loss. Even in the acceptance phase, you may continue to occasionally shed tears or otherwise show grief.

Anniversaries of the loss often will trigger periods of sadness. Once you have accepted your loss, you are able to see these anniversaries as opportunities to show the depth of your feelings for your losses. Other occasions also may remind you of your loss. These may include holidays or other special events. Each griever will experience these deep grieving occasions differently. Certain colors, foods, or aromas also may bring you back to deepest grief. Though these experiences will lessen in time, major losses will continue to have an impact on you throughout your life.

It helps to talk about these issues, rather than keeping them bottled up inside.

With acceptance you can plan for anniversaries, rather than be at their mercy. Many incarcerated men have looked back at their losses and seen a pattern . For example, one inmate saw how his grandfather's death in the month of October made the fall a season he dreaded. For several years, he had tried to live a sober life, but returned to drinking as the anniversary neared. He had believed that he could not handle the pain of his memories without alcohol.

When he wrote his "good-bye letter" to his grandfather, he was able to connect these two events. Once he did this, he was able to plan for the anniversary. In his case, he used this knowledge to alert his support group that a painful time was coming for him. After he was able to stay sober through the anniversary of his grandfather's death, he also felt closer to his memory.

What will the institutionalized boy gain from the acceptance of his loss? More than anything else, all of his experiences with acceptance (including being honest, owning his loss, valuing himself, and showing compassion for others) will open his ability to trust others again. By experiencing all of the grieving process, the boy will learn to trust. First, he learns to trust himself. Finally, he learns to choose trustworthy people in his life.

The Negative Aspects of Acceptance

The danger in all of the earlier stages of the grief cycle was becoming stuck, staying in a portion of the cycle long after it had outlived its usefulness to you.

The opposite problem can emerge in the acceptance phase. You may jump from protest to an artificial acceptance, trying to avoid the pain of grief proper.

Once you have learned about the fundamentals of the grief cycle, this may become a significant problem for you. As you review your grief issues, be certain you are giving yourself all the time you need in each area. If you jump from protest to acceptance, for example, you only will be cheating yourself of your growth.

Other than this possibility (jumping too quickly to acceptance), the acceptance phase of the cycle is very rich for the griever. Freed from the overwhelming aspects of grief proper, you can mourn creatively while gaining the strength you need to reinvest in society.

Exercises

1. **Active grievers, soldiers in combat, and women in labor, all report a similar experience. At the height of each of their different situations, they experience the sensation of being tossed around by forces beyond their control. This whirlwind of the grief-proper phase can be very frightening. However, for some it may seem calming at the same time.** *Have you allowed yourself to feel such a whirlwind of emotion in grieving? Describe it in detail, or write a story about a griever who has experienced this type of emotion.*

_____

_____

_____

_____

_____

_____

_____

_____

_____

_____

_____

_____

_____

2. What situations, losses, or other events have you fully accepted in your life? Allow yourself time to think before you answer these questions.

Event. (For example, "I lost all of the people and places that were familiar to me when my family moved from my hometown.")

a.

_____

_____

_____

_____

_____

_____

b.

_____

_____

_____

_____

_____

_____

c.

_____

_____

_____

_____

_____

_____

Timetable. (For example, "I pretended that I didn't care. I was angry at my parents. I finally accepted the change after spending my second Christmas in my new town.")

a.

_____

_____

_____

b.

_____

_____

_____

c.

_____

_____

_____

Length of time. (For example, 18 months)
a.

b.

c.

Use this format for several losses.

3. **Reread your good-bye letter (the one suggested in chapter four) once again, and answer the following questions.**
   Was I in grief proper when I wrote this?

_____

_____

_____

Am I still in grief proper at this time?

_____

_____

_____

What do I gain from staying in grief proper?

_____

_____

_____

What could I gain from moving on?

_____

_____

_____

Was I in the acceptance stage when I wrote this?

_____

_____

_____

If you feel you have completely accepted this loss, destroy the letter.

_____

_____

_____

Chapter Eight

Reinvestment and Resolution

Where are you in the grief process? To determine this, ask yourself, "Do I feel stronger than I have felt before?"

Your answer to this question should be very revealing. The grief process builds your self-esteem and your strength. You feel stronger—not shaky. If you are not feeling stronger, you may have jumped too fast into the acceptance phase.

Go back through the grief cycle. Ask yourself if you gave yourself enough time in each area. Again, be gentle with yourself. Old hurts do not disappear quickly. You deserve to feel the strength of personal acceptance. You deserve to be strong in your understanding of yourself.

I feel better. I'm on my square.

You will feel this strength because you have gone through a type of trial by fire. Like the clay pots the artist puts in the intense heat of his kiln, you will emerge changed, but stronger for the changes.

When we say a griever is ready to reinvest in life, we are speaking of the griever who already has been a part of society. For some incarcerated men, moving through the grief cycle may be their first opportunity to invest in society at all.

You can identify people who are invested in their society in many ways. As you read through this section, ask yourself how you might choose to invest in society after your release from prison.

People who are invested in their community care about what happens there. They participate in the process of change. Here are some of the ways they show their participation:

1. They are involved in:
   - political groups
   - religious groups
   - educational groups

They vote for the men and women who they believe can serve their community best. They participate in spiritual or religious groups and teach their beliefs to their children. They are active in groups that influence educators, such as the Parent-Teacher Association (PTA) or the school board.

2. They are involved in the physical appearance of their community. They spend time and energy keeping their community looking good. This may be as simple as picking up litter, shoveling snow so others can walk safely, or painting or repairing buildings.

3. They show concern for the people in their community by protecting the vulnerable members of it. They may volunteer to help the elderly or help establish a safe house for children. They may coach youngsters in sports or donate to organizations such as the United Way. They might give food to food banks or donate time in a shelter. If they have been incarcerated, they might speak to children about their experiences and offer advice.

Many incarcerated men have come to believe that this service work is "square" or only for the civilians and do-gooders. The news is, being "square" may not be all bad!

If you are sick and tired of playing cops and robbers, and finding yourself locked up one more time—you might be ready to invest in the "square" life.

Now, I know how I set myself up last time I got out. This time, I will be different.

Earlier discussions focused on comfort and fear being the twin forces that keep you stuck. Comfort and fear can keep you from investing in your community, as well. You always will find comfort in going back to the old crowd and the negative behaviors you are used to. It will be fearful for you to reach out to the community you used to rip off. But, once again, there is a payoff in working through your fear. It is increased self-esteem.

If you have been used to looking at other people as marks and suckers, this will be tough work for you. In fact, you clearly can see who the vulnerable people in your community are—look at who you have used for your own gain in the past. Who did you victimize? Have you gained any compassion for their pain by working through yours?

Poverty, racism, and violence are as American as apple pie. You may have used these issues to tell yourself that life was hopeless. This is a cop-out. While it is true that you alone cannot solve these problems, you can do your part.

You have made choices. You are not a victim—unless you decide to be one. Some men do leave prison stronger and healthier. They get out and stay out. They invest in life.

It will take time for your community to trust you. Friends, family, and strangers (like your parole officer or the cops from your precinct) will not jump to believe you have changed. Be prepared to be disbelieved. However, do not use other people's lack of confidence in you as an excuse to go back to your old beliefs. Prove them wrong! Success is the best revenge, but it takes time to be successful. Investing in life also means getting yourself a support system. You know where to find solid, trustworthy people. Just go to some of those places you used to avoid!

Pick a church, mosque, or temple for spiritual support. Follow your heart and your gut in this area. You will not be disappointed. Spiritually based people know about acceptance and forgiveness: some things you deserve. If the first spiritual group you approach does not feel right to you, find a different one. Most spiritual paths are paths in the right direction.

Spirituality does not necessarily come only from organized religions. Creativity is spiritual. If you cannot paint a picture, go to a museum. If you cannot carry a tune, play the radio loudly and sing along! Get a hobby. Go for a walk. Make a bird feeder. Hold a baby. Smile at a stranger. Look at the sunset, or listen hard when someone needs to be heard. These are all spiritual experiences if you are willing to let your spirit be touched by them.

If you are a recovering addict, get involved with a recovery group. Alcoholics Anonymous (AA) and Narcotics Anonymous (NA) are the grandfathers of these support groups. But if they do not fit for you, find one that does.

The Bar Across the Street   Reed

Take some positive risks for a change. You might be surprised at what you find.

If you are a veteran, find out about veterans' groups. The people you will meet can be a great support to you, and the grief work you have done will help you connect with them. If you have been diagnosed as having Post Traumatic Stress Disorder (PTSD) as a result of your military experiences, you may have avoided veterans' groups in the past. Give them a chance again. Your grief work may have given you a new perspective.

Words can't express how good I feel about the person I have become.

Think about getting professional help, if you know you need it. Men's groups or one-on-one counseling may be free to you or available on a sliding-fee scale. Asking for help is a part of your investment in yourself. Knowing you need help is a sign you are getting healthy.

If you want to continue your grief work in a positive atmosphere, check out grief groups. Most large hospitals have ongoing grief groups. Take the risk if you want the help.

Most importantly, do not give up on yourself. As long as you are alive, there is hope. People do not suddenly get done with growing up. Growth is a life-long and life-satisfying process.

Congratulations on having the guts to stick with your grief work and finish this workbook. Best of luck as you continue in life. Take your time. Ask for help. Stay free.

_____

Exercises

1. How will you invest in your community? Be specific.

_____

_____

_____

_____

_____

_____

_____

_____

2. How will you invest in yourself? Be specific.

_____

_____

_____

_____

_____

_____

_____

_____

_____

3. **Did your view of yourself and your world change as you read this workbook? How has it changed?**

_____

_____

_____

_____

_____

_____

_____

_____

4. **Write a good-bye letter for each loss you have been working on (For example: good-bye to my first love, good-bye to alcohol and other drugs, good-bye to my deceased loved one, good-bye to my physical health). As each letter is completed, read it for the signs of each phase of the grief cycle. If you believe you have completed the cycle, destroy the letter.**

_____

_____

_____

_____

_____

_____

_____

_____

_____

_____

_____

_____

_____

_____

_____

_____

_____

_____

_____

_____

_____

_____

_____

_____

_____

_____

_____

_____

_____

_____

_____

_____

_____

If you still need to work on the issue, keep the letter until it is resolved. As you complete each task, pat yourself on the back for your good work and the courage to change.

Suggested Reading

Many of these books are found in prison libraries or are available on interlibrary loan. Invest in yourself.

Fromm, Erich. 1947. *Man for Himself.* New York: Rinehart.

———. 1956. *The Art of Loving.* New York: Harper.

James, John and Cherry, Frank. 1988. *The Grief Recovery Handbook.* New York: Harper and Row.

Kubler-Ross, Elisabeth. 1969. *On Death and Dying.* New York: Macmillan.

Kushner, Harold. 1981. *When Bad Things Happen to Good People.* New York: Schocken Books.

Lewis, C. S. 1963. *A Grief Observed.* New York: Seabury Press.

Westberg, Granger. 1962. *Good Grief.* Philadelphia: Fortress Press.

About the Author

Beverly Kay Welo is a corrections program therapist at the Lino Lakes Correctional Facility in Minnesota. She began her career in corrections as a chemical dependency counselor after graduation from the St. Mary's Campus of the College of St. Catherine's Chemical Dependency and Family Treatment Program in Minneapolis, Minnesota.

Since the publication of *Life Beyond Loss*, Ms. Welo has lectured extensively. Her workshop, Raging Grievers, has been presented to hundreds of professionals in the fields of corrections, chemical dependency, social work, and family therapy.

Ms. Welo is married and the mother of three children.

The author welcomes comments on the use of this manual from professionals and inmates. Send comments to Beverly Kay Welo, Corrections Program Therapist, Lino Lakes Correctional Facility, 7525 4th Avenue, Lino Lakes, Minnesota 55014.